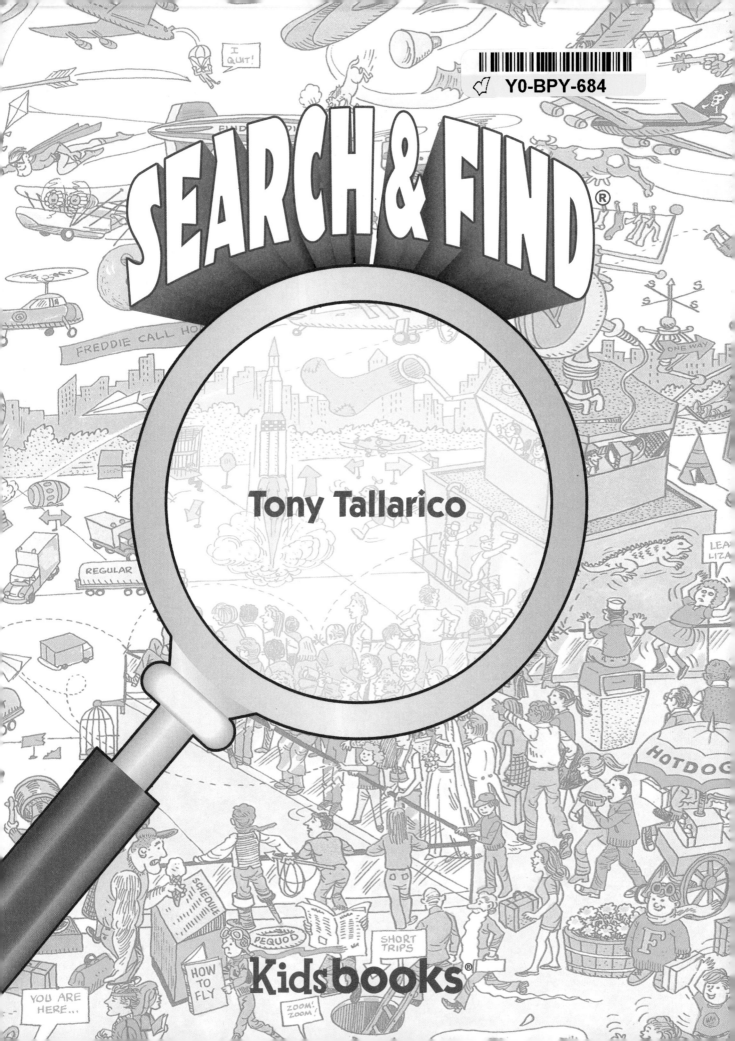

# FIND FREDDIE

WHERE ARE THEY?

Find Freddie along with hundreds of other zany things in these hilarious scenes.

- Uncle Sam at the ballpark
- Cowboys on the beach
- Humpty Dumpty in Monsterville
- Flying fish in space
- Peanuts at the museum
- Rabbits at school
- Flying saucers in the Old West

. . . and lots more!

# Find Freddie at
# Home
### and...

- ☐ "8 Up" can
- ☐ Alarm clock
- ☑ Arrow
- ☑ Baseball trophy
- ☐ Birdcage
- ☐ Bow tie
- ☐ Broken heart
- ☑ "Call Joe"
- ☐ Drum
- ☐ Elephant head
- ☐ Fake teeth
- ☐ Harmonica
- ☐ Hockey stick
- ☑ "How to Play" book
- ☑ "Junk Mail"
- ☐ Light switch
- ☐ Monster foot
- ☐ Orange-and-green lamp
- ☐ Paper airplanes (5)
- ☐ Peanuts
- ☐ Baseball player
- ☐ picture
- ☐ Popcorn
- ☐ Record
- ☐ Skulls (2)
- ☐ Straws (2)
- ☑ Sunglasses
- ☑ Telescope
- ☑ Tire swing

# Find Freddie in
# Space
## and...

- ☑ Angel
- ☐ Balloon
- ☐ Basketball
- ☐ Bathtub
- ☐ Cannon
- ☐ Dogcatcher
- ☐ Doghouse
- ☐ Dragon
- ☐ Envelope
- ☑ Flying school bus
- ☐ Garbage truck
- ☐ Gorilla
- ☐ Hammer
- ☐ Mary Poppins
- ☐ Meatball
- ☑ "Meteor shower"
- ☐ NASA parachute
- ☐ Necktie
- ☐ Pencil
- ☐ Pink elephant
- ☐ Pinocchio
- ☐ "Planet of the Foot" (2)
- ☐ Polka-dot shorts
- ☐ Pyramid
- ☐ Red spray paint
- ☐ Rocking chair
- ☑ Scissors
- ☐ Slingshot
- ☐ Top hat
- ☐ Traffic light
- ☐ Trash can

# Find Freddie at the **Beach** and...

- ☐ Barrel
- ☐ Clothespin
- ☐ Duck
- ☐ Eight ball
- ☐ Elephant
- ☐ Fishing cat
- ☐ Flamingo
- ☐ Flying car
- ☐ "Fresh Sand"
- ☐ Giant sandwich
- ☐ Golfers (2)
- ☐ Handstand surfer
- ☐ Helicopter
- ☐ Horse
- ☐ Lighthouse
- ☐ Lion
- ☐ Mice (2)
- ☐ Motorcycle
- ☐ Native American
- ☐ Open umbrellas (6)
- ☐ Rocket
- ☐ Rowboat
- ☐ Scuba diver
- ☐ Sheriff
- ☐ Shovel
- ☐ Snowshoes (2)
- ☐ Starfish (2)
- ☐ Strongman
- ☐ Tent
- ☐ Watering can
- ☐ Witch

# Find Freddie
## at
## School
### and...

- [ ] Air pump
- [ ] Barbells (2)
- [ ] Baseballs (2)
- [ ] Basketballs (3)
- [ ] Bench
- [ ] Briefcases (2)
- [ ] Broken windows (2)
- [ ] Butterfly net
- [ ] Fish (2)
- [ ] Fishing pole
- [ ] Horse
- [ ] Magic carpet
- [ ] Mail carrier
- [ ] Mouse
- [ ] Mud puddle
- [ ] Music notes (2)
- [ ] Paper airplanes (5)
- [ ] Pillow
- [ ] Rabbits (2)
- [ ] "Report Card"
- [ ] Skull
- [ ] Soccer ball
- [ ] Swing set
- [ ] Telescope
- [ ] Trash can
- [ ] Tug-of-war
- [ ] Upside-down bucket
- [ ] Window washer

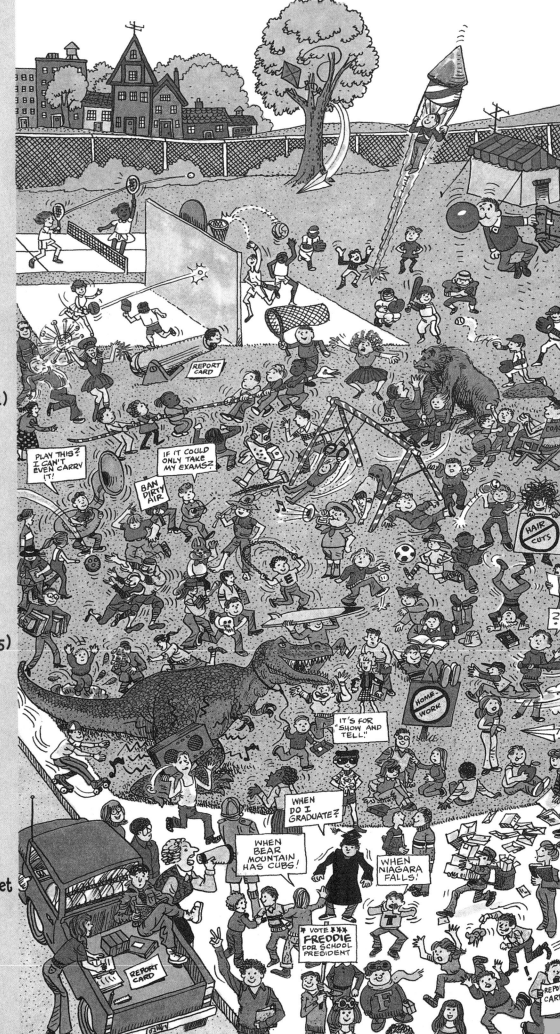

# Find Freddie on the
## School
## Bus Trip
### and...

- ☐ Barn
- ☐ Baseball bat
- ☐ Basketball court
- ☐ "Clean Me"
- ☐ Dogs (2)
- ☐ Elephant
- ☐ Flying bat
- ☐ Football
- ☐ Frankenstein's monster
- ☐ Giraffe
- ☐ Horse
- ☐ Hot dog mobile
- ☐ Jack-o'-lantern
- ☐ Moose head
- ☐ Pig
- ☐ Pizza truck
- ☐ Rowboat
- ☐ Santa Claus
- ☐ Scarecrow
- ☐ Snake
- ☐ Swimming pool
- ☐ Tennis court
- ☐ Tent
- ☐ Tic-tac-toe
- ☐ Tombstone
- ☐ Traffic cop
- ☐ Turtle
- ☐ Umbrellas (2)
- ☐ U-shaped building

# Find Freddie
in
## Monsterville
and...

- [ ] Broken heart
- [ ] Cowboy hat
- [ ] Flowers (2)
- [ ] "For Rent"
- [ ] Gorilla
- [ ] Hose
- [ ] Key
- [ ] Mouse hole
- [ ] Ms. Transylvania
- [ ] Mummy
- [ ] Number 13 (3)
- [ ] One-eyed monster
- [ ] Owl
- [ ] Parachute
- [ ] Pig
- [ ] Pile of bones
- [ ] Pink hand
- [ ] Pyramid
- [ ] Rat
- [ ] Scary trees (2)
- [ ] Skeleton
- [ ] Skulls (8)
- [ ] Stethoscope
- [ ] Three-legged ghost
- [ ] Tin can
- [ ] Tin man
- [ ] Trick-or-Treat bags (4)
- [ ] Weather vane

# Find Freddie at the Airport and...

- ☐ Binoculars
- ☐ Birdcage
- ☐ Chair
- ☐ Clothespins (6)
- ☐ Football
- ☐ Golf club
- ☐ Green checkered pants
- ☐ Guardhouse
- ☐ Hammock
- ☐ Harpoon
- ☐ Hearts (2)
- ☐ Helicopters
- ☐ Hot-air balloon
- ☐ Hot dogs (2)
- ☐ Ice-cream cones (2)
- ☐ Kite
- ☐ Laundry line
- ☐ Locomotive
- ☐ Lost wallet
- ☐ Manhole
- ☐ Paint rollers (2)
- ☐ Parachute
- ☐ Pear
- ☐ "Pequod"
- ☐ Pizza
- ☐ Roller coaster
- ☐ Skier
- ☐ Stretch limo
- ☐ Submarine
- ☐ Toaster

# Find Freddie at the **Ballpark** and...

- ☐ Balloons (7)
- ☐ Banana
- ☐ Baseball bats (10)
- ☐ Basketball hoop
- ☐ Bicycle
- ☐ Binoculars
- ☐ Blimp
- ☐ Carrot
- ☐ Clipboard
- ☐ Cook
- ☐ Cowboy hat
- ☐ Detour
- ☐ Dogs (2)
- ☐ Kite
- ☐ Ladder
- ☐ Lawn mower
- ☐ Money
- ☐ Mouse hole
- ☐ Periscope
- ☐ Pickax
- ☐ Policemen (2)
- ☐ Ripped pants
- ☐ Sombrero
- ☐ Sunbather
- ☐ Sword
- ☐ Toolbox
- ☐ Trash can
- ☐ Turtle
- ☐ Upside-down fan

# Find Freddie at the **Museum** and...

- ☐ Airplane
- ☐ Alien
- ☐ Balloons (7)
- ☐ Bather
- ☐ Birdcage
- ☐ Birthday cake
- ☐ Doctor
- ☐ Doghouse
- ☐ Firefighter
- ☐ Fire hydrant
- ☐ "First Prize"
- ☐ Fishing pole
- ☐ Flying carpet
- ☐ Football player
- ☐ Guitar
- ☐ Headless man
- ☐ Hot-air balloon
- ☐ Ice-cream cone
- ☐ Jack-in-the-box
- ☐ Kite
- ☐ Knights (2)
- ☐ Long beard
- ☐ Magnifying glass
- ☐ Princess
- ☐ Quicksand
- ☐ Robin Hood
- ☐ Scuba diver
- ☐ Superman
- ☐ TV antenna
- ☐ Viking ship
- ☐ Watering can
- ☐ Whistle

# Find Freddie in the Old West Town and...

- [ ] Angel
- [ ] Apple
- [ ] Arrows (2)
- [ ] Artist
- [ ] Baby turtle
- [ ] Camel
- [ ] Elephant
- [ ] Fire hydrant
- [ ] Fishing pole
- [ ] Flowerpot
- [ ] Football
- [ ] Guitar
- [ ] "ICU2"
- [ ] Monster hand
- [ ] Mouse holes (2)
- [ ] Outhouse
- [ ] Periscope
- [ ] Piano
- [ ] Pink elephant
- [ ] Sailboat
- [ ] Saw
- [ ] Smoke signal
- [ ] Stop sign
- [ ] Sun
- [ ] Toasters (5)
- [ ] UFO
- [ ] Umbrellas (2)
- [ ] Upside-down sign
- [ ] "Wet Paint"

FIND FREDDIE     LOOK FOR LISA     HUNT FOR HECTOR     SEARCH FOR SAM

# HUNT FOR HECTOR

WHERE ARE THEY?

Where's Hector?
You'll have to search through these
wacky scenes—and more—to find him!

◎ Cats at the Dog Mall
◎ K-9 secret agents
◎ Fencing dogs at the Olympics
◎ Fire hydrants in Dogtown
◎ Bones at the Hall of Fame
◎ Dancing dogs at school
◎ Hot dogs in space

. . . and lots more!

# Hunt for **Hector** at the **Dog Hall** of **Fame** and...

- ☐ Baby kangaroo
- ☐ "Bach Beagle"
- ☐ Beard
- ☐ Birds (2)
- ☐ Chef
- ☐ Dog bowl
- ☐ Dogcatcher
- ☐ Dog stamp
- ☐ Eyeglasses (3)
- ☐ Fire hydrant
- ☐ Football helmet
- ☐ Hearts (3)
- ☐ Hot-air balloon
- ☐ Mailbag
- ☐ Moon
- ☐ Mouse hole
- ☐ Music note
- ☐ Oversized tie
- ☐ Pilgrim hat
- ☐ Police dogs (2)
- ☐ Space dog
- ☐ Stars (20)
- ☐ Stool
- ☐ Target
- ☐ Top hat
- ☐ Umpire
- ☐ "Unidog"

# Hunt for Hector at Dog School and...

- ☐ "Barking King I"
- ☐ Briefcases (3)
- ☐ Canes (2)
- ☐ Cat litter
- ☐ Crown
- ☐ Crying dog
- ☐ "Dog Days"
- ☐ "Doggy Decimal System"
- ☐ "Dog Tail"
- ☐ Easel
- ☐ Empty dog bowls (14)
- ☐ Fire hydrant
- ☐ Graduate's hat
- ☐ Hammer
- ☐ Ladle
- ☐ Man on leash
- ☐ Napkins (2)
- ☐ Paintbrush
- ☐ Pearl necklace
- ☐ Roller skates
- ☐ Ruler
- ☐ Screwdriver
- ☐ Sleeping dog
- ☐ Spoons (3)
- ☐ Stool
- ☐ Straw
- ☐ "Super Dog"

# Hunt for Hector
among the
## Dogcatchers
and...

- ☐ Airplane
- ☐ Bathing dog
- ☐ Briefcase
- ☐ Car antenna
- ☐ Cats (5)
- ☐ Convertible car
- ☐ "Dog mail"
- ☐ Dollar signs (11)
- ☐ Empty bowls (2)
- ☐ Fire hose
- ☐ Fire truck
- ☐ Fishing pole
- ☐ Guitar
- ☐ Heart
- ☐ Manhole
- ☐ Music note
- ☐ Net
- ☐ "P.D." (7)
- ☐ Piano
- ☐ Pink hats (8)
- ☐ Rope swing
- ☐ Satellite dish
- ☐ Sirens (2)
- ☐ Turtle
- ☐ "UDS"
- ☐ Umbrella
- ☐ Watermelon
- ☐ Water tower

# Hunt for Hector at the K-9 Clean up and...

- ☐ Anchor
- ☐ Bones (2)
- ☐ Broken piggy bank
- ☐ Butterfly net
- ☐ Cane
- ☐ Chimney
- ☐ "Chow" bowl
- ☐ Cowboy hat
- ☐ Doorbell
- ☐ Duck
- ☐ Fake mustache
- ☐ Feather
- ☐ Fire hose
- ☐ Fire hydrants (3)
- ☐ Fishing pole
- ☐ Helicopter
- ☐ "K-9" helmet
- ☐ Manhole cover
- ☐ Motorcycle
- ☐ Pails of water (7)
- ☐ Parachute
- ☐ Penguin
- ☐ Rope ladder
- ☐ Rowboat
- ☐ Sailor's hat
- ☐ Scrub brush
- ☐ Skateboard
- ☐ "S.S. Poseidon"
- ☐ Superpooch
- ☐ Tin cans (4)

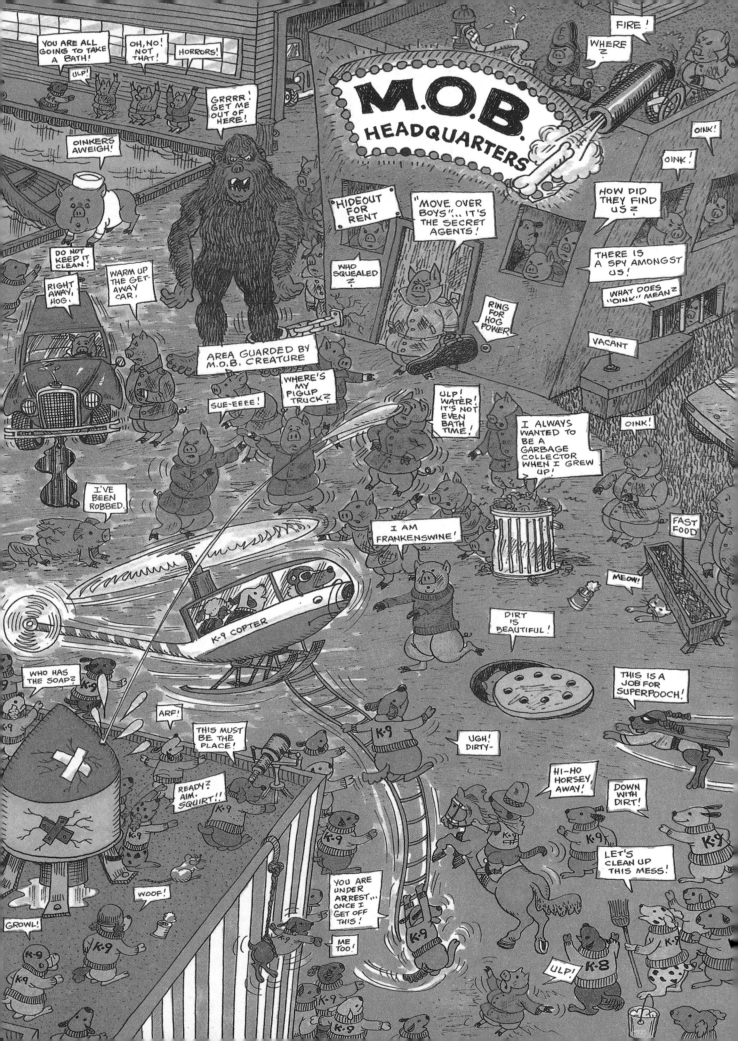

# Hunt for Hector at the Super Dog Bowl and...

- ☐ "107"
- ☐ Bandaged tail
- ☐ Bench
- ☐ Binoculars
- ☐ Cactus
- ☐ Cracked egg
- ☐ Daisies (3)
- ☐ Dog pile
- ☐ Electrical outlet
- ☐ Footballs (2)
- ☐ Heart-shaped turf
- ☐ Jack-o'-lanterns (5)
- ☐ "Last T.D."
- ☐ Manhole
- ☐ "No Ball Playing"
- ☐ Paint can
- ☐ Patched pants
- ☐ Pirate hat
- ☐ Pom-poms (2)
- ☐ Referees (2)
- ☐ Rooster
- ☐ Sleepy dogs (2)
- ☐ Star
- ☐ Sword
- ☐ Target
- ☐ TV set
- ☐ Water dog
- ☐ Worm

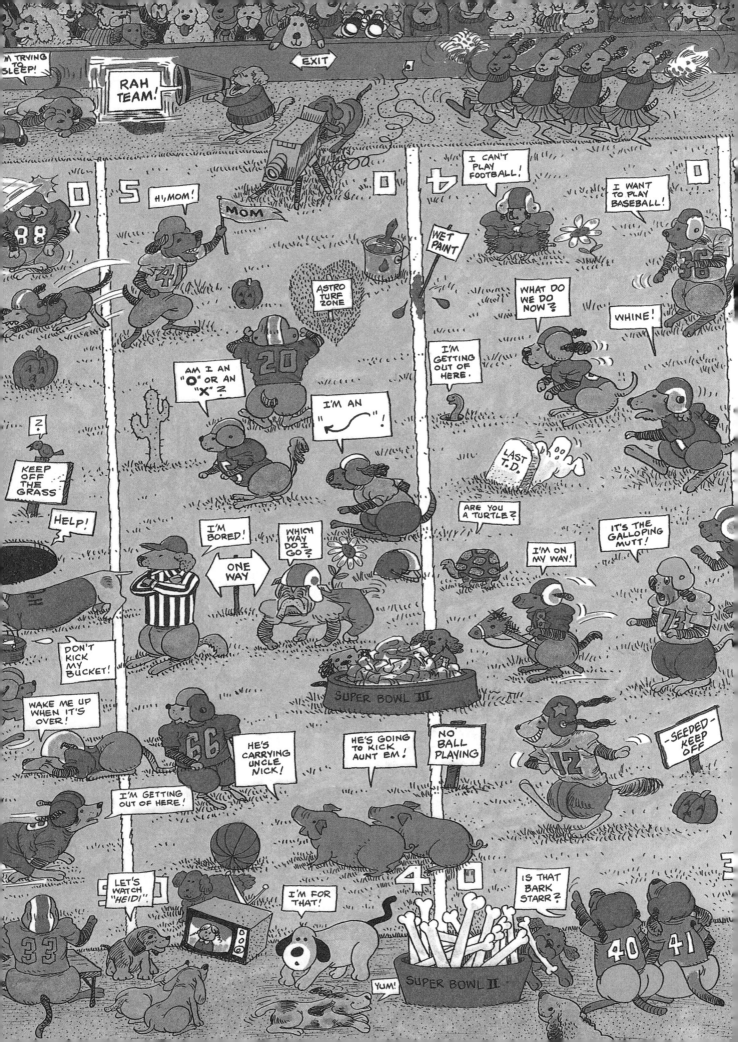

# Hunt for Hector
## at the
# Dog Mall
### and...

- ☐ Air conditioner
- ☐ Barber's pole
- ☐ Baseball
- ☐ Bone cake
- ☐ "Bone on a Bun"
- ☐ Bookstore
- ☐ Car
- ☐ Cats (2)
- ☐ Chef's hat
- ☐ Crooked chimney
- ☐ Doghouse
- ☐ Dog in shining armor
- ☐ Fire hydrants (2)
- ☐ Food court
- ☐ "For Rent"
- ☐ Graduate
- ☐ Hockey stick
- ☐ "Hunk" poster
- ☐ Leashes (3)
- ☐ Mug
- ☐ Newspaper seller
- ☐ Scissors
- ☐ Spotlight
- ☐ Suitcase
- ☐ Trophy
- ☐ Turkey
- ☐ Witch dog

# Hunt for **Hector**
## at the
# Dog
# Olympics
### and...

- ☐ Bone bat
- ☐ Bow
- ☐ Bowling ball
- ☐ Broom
- ☐ Bucket
- ☐ Clipboard
- ☐ Diving board
- ☐ Fallen skater
- ☐ Fencing swords (2)
- ☐ Fishing pole
- ☐ Football players (3)
- ☐ Golf tee
- ☐ Hat with propeller
- ☐ Home plate
- ☐ Ice skates (14)
- ☐ Karate dog
- ☐ Ping-Pong paddle
- ☐ Pitcher
- ☐ Pole-vaulter
- ☐ Race car
- ☐ Ski jumper
- ☐ Stop sign
- ☐ Target
- ☐ Tennis racket
- ☐ Top hat
- ☐ Trainer
- ☐ TV camera
- ☐ Volleyball
- ☐ Weight lifter
- ☐ Yo-yo

# Hunt for Hector at the **TV Quiz Show** and...

- [ ] Announcer
- [ ] "Arf TV" (3)
- [ ] Baseball cap
- [ ] Boxes (3)
- [ ] Camera
- [ ] Chef
- [ ] Clipboard
- [ ] Clothespins (2)
- [ ] Coat
- [ ] Contestants (4)
- [ ] Crown
- [ ] Director slate
- [ ] Dog collar
- [ ] Dog food
- [ ] Drum
- [ ] "Exit"
- [ ] Flashlight
- [ ] Flowerpot
- [ ] Game wheel
- [ ] Gorilla
- [ ] Headphones (5)
- [ ] Magic wand
- [ ] Megaphone
- [ ] Pencil
- [ ] Pile of bones
- [ ] Space dog
- [ ] Stacks of money (5)
- [ ] Trumpet

# Hunt for Hector
## in
# Space
### and...

- ☐ Bench
- ☐ Blimp
- ☐ Bone antenna
- ☐ Bone smokestack
- ☐ Bus
- ☐ Cars (3)
- ☐ Diving board
- ☐ "Dog fish"
- ☐ Dog in trash can
- ☐ "Dog paddle"
- ☐ Earth
- ☐ Emergency dog
- ☐ Graduate dog
- ☐ Heart with arrow
- ☐ Hot dog
- ☐ Juggler
- ☐ Mailbag
- ☐ Nut
- ☐ Old tire
- ☐ Pizza
- ☐ Pluto
- ☐ Pup in a cup
- ☐ Roller coaster
- ☐ Space map
- ☐ Star with tail
- ☐ Top hat
- ☐ UFO
- ☐ Unicycle

# Hunt for Hector
## in
# Dogtown
### and...

- ☐ Baby carriage
- ☐ "Bark Your Horn"
- ☐ Basketball
- ☐ Bicycle
- ☐ Birds (2)
- ☐ Chimneys (8)
- ☐ Crossing guard
- ☐ Dog bones (13)
- ☐ "Dog cookies"
- ☐ Dog fountain
- ☐ Falling "G"
- ☐ Gas pump
- ☐ Hammer
- ☐ Human on leash
- ☐ Mailbox
- ☐ Manhole
- ☐ Sailor
- ☐ Screwdriver
- ☐ Skateboard
- ☐ Soccer ball
- ☐ Streetlight
- ☐ Super Dog
- ☐ Swimming pool
- ☐ Trash cans (2)
- ☐ TV
- ☐ Wrench

**HUNT FOR HECTOR**

**SEARCH FOR SAM**

**FIND FREDDIE**

**LOOK FOR LISA**

# LOOK FOR LISA

WHERE ARE THEY?

Look for Lisa in all sorts of crazy places!
While you're looking,
you'll see crazy things, such as:

- Hippos at a rock concert
- Cactuses on the beach
- Parrots in the library
- Surfers on a farm
- Frogs at the flea market
- Snow White at the marathon
- Unicorns in Utah

. . . and much, much more!

# Look for Lisa at the Marathon and...

- ☐ Angel
- ☐ Barrel
- ☐ Basketball
- ☐ Bucket
- ☐ Cane
- ☐ Chef
- ☐ Cowboy
- ☐ Deer
- ☐ Diving board
- ☐ Doctor
- ☐ Ice-cream cone
- ☐ Kite
- ☐ Monsters (2)
- ☐ Motorcycle
- ☐ Native American
- ☐ Net
- ☐ Periscope
- ☐ Policeman
- ☐ Rocket
- ☐ Roller skates
- ☐ Sad face
- ☐ Scooter
- ☐ Shortcut
- ☐ Sombrero
- ☐ Speed skater
- ☐ Spotted dog
- ☐ Strongman
- ☐ Surfer
- ☐ Taxi
- ☐ Tuba
- ☐ Umbrella

# Look for Lisa
## After School and...

# Look for Lisa at the Rock Concert and...

- ☐ Alien
- ☐ Ape
- ☐ Balloons (6)
- ☐ Barbell
- ☐ Bowling ball
- ☐ Doctor
- ☐ Fish tank
- ☐ Flamingo
- ☐ Flowers
- ☐ Gorilla
- ☐ Hot-dog stand
- ☐ Knight
- ☐ Lamppost
- ☐ Masked man
- ☐ Moon
- ☐ Mummy
- ☐ Net
- ☐ Painter
- ☐ Prisoner
- ☐ Rabbit
- ☐ Snowman
- ☐ Stack of pizza boxes
- ☐ Stars (6)
- ☐ Tin man
- ☐ Tombstones (2)
- ☐ Trampoline
- ☐ Waiter

# Look for **Lisa** on the **Farm** and...

- ☐ Boat
- ☐ Cactus
- ☐ Cave
- ☐ Clouds (3)
- ☐ Donkey
- ☐ "Don't Stop" sign
- ☐ Egg
- ☐ Elephant
- ☐ Eskimo
- ☐ Finish line
- ☐ Ghost
- ☐ Giant pumpkin
- ☐ "Grade A"
- ☐ Log pile
- ☐ Message in a bottle
- ☐ Net
- ☐ Periscope
- ☐ Pitchfork
- ☐ Policeman
- ☐ Prisoner
- ☐ Scuba diver
- ☐ Stop sign
- ☐ "Summer"
- ☐ Surfboards (2)
- ☐ Tent
- ☐ Water bucket
- ☐ Weather vane

# Look for Lisa
at the
# Beach
and...

- ☐ Beach ball
- ☐ Broken surfboard
- ☐ Broom
- ☐ Bunch of balloons
- ☐ Castle
- ☐ Cello
- ☐ Cruise ship
- ☐ Diving board
- ☐ Frisbee
- ☐ Hearts (3)
- ☐ Horse
- ☐ Jack-in-the-box
- ☐ Kite
- ☐ Lifeguard
- ☐ Lost swim trunks
- ☐ Lunch box
- ☐ Merman
- ☐ Palm trees (3)
- ☐ Pickle barrel
- ☐ Policeman
- ☐ Sailboat
- ☐ Sailors (2)
- ☐ Sea serpent
- ☐ Starfish (9)
- ☐ Swans (2)
- ☐ Trash can
- ☐ Turtle
- ☐ Whale

## Look for **Lisa** at the **Big Sale** and...

## Look for **Lisa** around the **World** and...

- [ ] Airplane
- [ ] Castle
- [ ] Cruise ship
- [ ] Elephant
- [ ] Fisherman
- [ ] Flamingo
- [ ] Foot
- [ ] Golf club
- [ ] Guitar
- [ ] Horse
- [ ] Hot-air balloon
- [ ] Ladder
- [ ] Movie camera
- [ ] Palm trees (3)
- [ ] Pine trees (6)
- [ ] Pizza man
- [ ] Refrigerator
- [ ] Santa Claus
- [ ] Scarves (2)
- [ ] Seal
- [ ] Sea monster
- [ ] Skis (8)
- [ ] Snowball
- [ ] Sombrero
- [ ] Surfboards (3)
- [ ] UFOs (2)

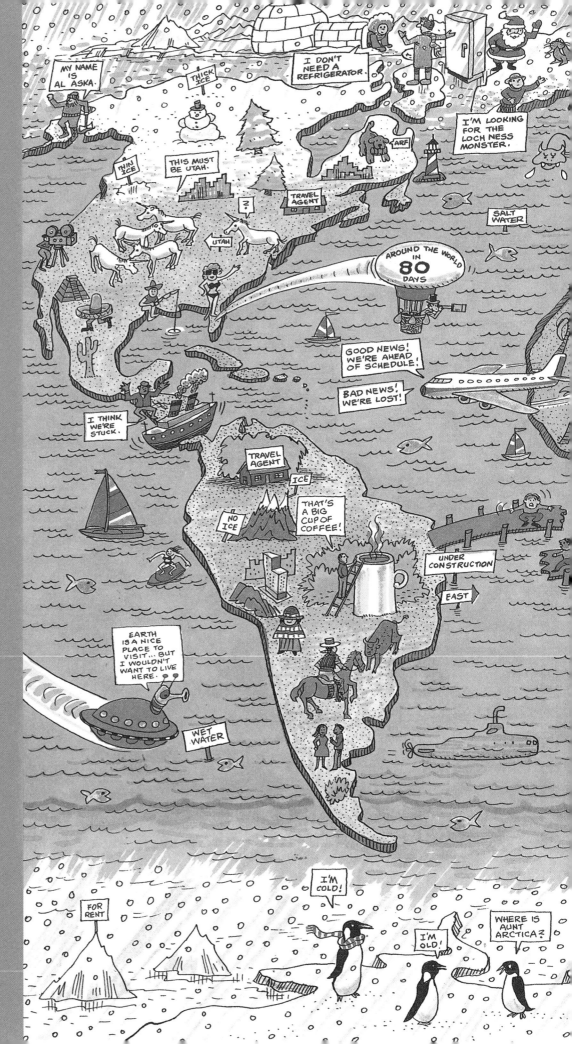

# Look for **Lisa** at the **Library** and...

- [ ] Baseball
- [ ] Birdcage
- [ ] Bowling pins (10)
- [ ] Brooms (2)
- [ ] Cactus
- [ ] Cactus book
- [ ] Cake
- [ ] Campfire
- [ ] Candle
- [ ] Car
- [ ] Football player
- [ ] Frowning books (2)
- [ ] Frying pan
- [ ] Globe
- [ ] Hearts (4)
- [ ] Hot dog
- [ ] Jack-in-the-box
- [ ] Knight
- [ ] Monster hands (3)
- [ ] Music note
- [ ] Napoleon
- [ ] Old tire
- [ ] Pole-vaulter
- [ ] Policewoman
- [ ] "Quiet" signs (6)
- [ ] Smiley face
- [ ] Teapot
- [ ] Trap door
- [ ] Tricycle
- [ ] Wagon
- [ ] Witch

# Look for **Lisa** at the **Amusement Park** and...

# Look for Lisa at the Flea Market and...

- ☐ Birdcages (2)
- ☐ Clown
- ☐ Court jester
- ☐ Cowboy hat
- ☐ Crown
- ☐ Elephant
- ☐ Elf
- ☐ Fishing hook
- ☐ Football
- ☐ Golf club
- ☐ Horse
- ☐ Map
- ☐ Monster
- ☐ Old tire
- ☐ Paintbrush
- ☐ Pear
- ☐ Records (8)
- ☐ Sailor
- ☐ Sailor hat
- ☐ Santa hat
- ☐ Scuba diver
- ☐ Shopping bag
- ☐ Skateboard
- ☐ Telephone booth
- ☐ Train conductor
- ☐ Wheelbarrow
- ☐ Witch

# Look for Lisa as the Circus Comes to Town and...

- ☐ Aliens (2)
- ☐ Arrows (8)
- ☐ Barbell
- ☐ Bass drum
- ☐ Bone
- ☐ Broom
- ☐ Cowboys (4)
- ☐ Crown
- ☐ "Enter"
- ☐ Flags (6)
- ☐ Frankenstein's monster
- ☐ Hole
- ☐ Juggler
- ☐ Music note
- ☐ Net
- ☐ Plates (7)
- ☐ Police officers (2)
- ☐ Poodle
- ☐ Sad face
- ☐ Soldiers (2)
- ☐ Stroller
- ☐ Unicorn
- ☐ Unicycle
- ☐ Upside-down sign
- ☐ Whistle
- ☐ Witch

LOOK FOR LISA    FIND FREDDIE    SEARCH FOR SAM    HUNT FOR HECTOR

# SEARCH FOR SAM

Sam's a sly cat, so good luck in your search!
You'll encounter hilarious characters in strange
scenes as you search for Sam.

- Dogs at the cat show
- Rhinos at the disco
- Alley cats in ancient Egypt
- Meows at midnight
- Fat cats at the gym
- Sharks in Cat City
- Dogbusters

. . . and lots more!

# Search for Sam
## in
## Cat City
### and...

- ☐ Airplane
- ☐ Antenna
- ☐ Balloons (2)
- ☐ Barrel
- ☐ Blimp
- ☐ Candle
- ☐ Cracked window
- ☐ Elephant
- ☐ Fire hydrant
- ☐ Fur coat
- ☐ Hammer
- ☐ Hard hats (3)
- ☐ Mailbox
- ☐ Manhole cover
- ☐ Motorcycle
- ☐ Music notes (8)
- ☐ Octopus
- ☐ Red bow
- ☐ Rocket
- ☐ Rooster
- ☐ Shovel
- ☐ Sun
- ☐ Telephone booth
- ☐ Toolbox
- ☐ Towel
- ☐ Turtle
- ☐ Waiter

## Search for Sam
### on
# Friday the
# 13th
#### and...

- [ ] Black cats (4)
- [ ] Bow tie
- [ ] Candy cane
- [ ] Clock
- [ ] Clothesline
- [ ] Count Dracula
- [ ] Count Dracula Jr.
- [ ] Cow
- [ ] Cracked mirror
- [ ] Doctor
- [ ] Eye patch
- [ ] Fish
- [ ] Flying witch
- [ ] Football
- [ ] Headless man
- [ ] Head looking
      for body
- [ ] Horse and carriage
- [ ] Kite
- [ ] Magic carpet
- [ ] One-eyed
      monsters (2)
- [ ] Painter
- [ ] Pig
- [ ] Quicksand
- [ ] Rabbit
- [ ] Sailboat
- [ ] Turtle
- [ ] Two-faced man
- [ ] Wooden leg

# Search for Sam at
# Fat Cat Gym
### and...

- ☐ Book
- ☐ Breaking rope
- ☐ Burned feet
- ☐ Cat food dish
- ☐ Catnap
- ☐ Clipboard
- ☐ Cool cat
- ☐ Dog bone
- ☐ "Do Not Touch"
- ☐ Escaped bird
- ☐ Fish (2)
- ☐ Fishbowl
- ☐ Hearts (3)
- ☐ Helmet
- ☐ Jump rope
- ☐ Money
- ☐ Pair of boxing gloves
- ☐ Pizza
- ☐ Prisoner
- ☐ Punching bags (2)
- ☐ Rats (3)
- ☐ Roller skates (2)
- ☐ Stationary bike
- ☐ Sweat bands (12)
- ☐ Tail warmer
- ☐ Window
- ☐ Yoga mats (3)

# Search for Sam at the
# Midnight
# Meowing
### and...

- [ ] Baseball
- [ ] Bat
- [ ] Birdhouse
- [ ] Can
- [ ] Cannon
- [ ] Cloud
- [ ] Fishbowl
- [ ] Fish skeletons (2)
- [ ] Football
- [ ] Gate
- [ ] Jack-o'-lantern
- [ ] Light
- [ ] Microphone
- [ ] Moon
- [ ] "No Welcome" mat
- [ ] Old tire
- [ ] Police car
- [ ] Policeman
- [ ] Pot
- [ ] Record player
- [ ] Rolling pin
- [ ] Spoon
- [ ] Stacks of paper (2)
- [ ] Stars (4)
- [ ] Table
- [ ] Tent
- [ ] UFO
- [ ] Wood planks (3)
- [ ] Yo-yo

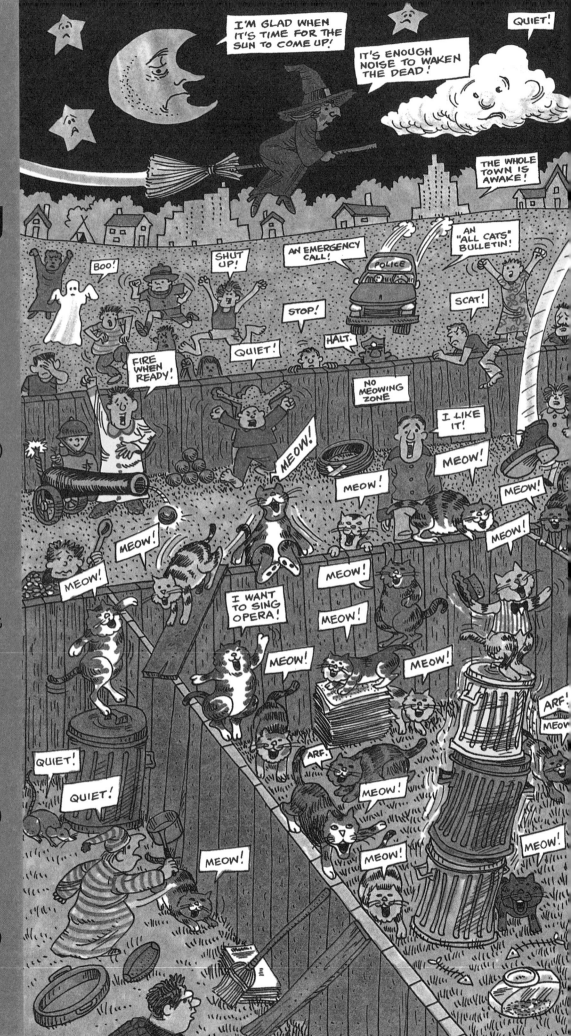

# Search for Sam
## at the
# Disco
### and...

- ☐ Ballerina
- ☐ Blue rhinos (2)
- ☐ Breakdance cat
- ☐ Cat blowing horn
- ☐ Chef
- ☐ Clown cat
- ☐ Cowboy cat
- ☐ Disco ball
- ☐ Duck
- ☐ Earplug seller
- ☐ Earrings
- ☐ Eye patch
- ☐ Flowerpot
- ☐ Hard hat
- ☐ Karate cat
- ☐ Lampshade
- ☐ Native American cat
- ☐ Pig
- ☐ Pirate sword
- ☐ Police officer
- ☐ Roller skates
- ☐ Skis
- ☐ Snow cat
- ☐ Speakers (10)
- ☐ Sunglasses
- ☐ Swinging cat
- ☐ Top hat
- ☐ Wooden leg

# Search for Sam at the Battle of Cats and Mice and...

- ☐ Bird
- ☐ Birdhouse
- ☐ Broom
- ☐ Catalog
- ☐ Chimney
- ☐ Dog bone
- ☐ "Exit"
- ☐ Feather
- ☐ Fire hose
- ☐ Fishing pole
- ☐ Football
- ☐ Karate Kat
- ☐ Medal
- ☐ Mug
- ☐ Mummy
- ☐ Owl
- ☐ Pickle
- ☐ Rabbit
- ☐ Rolling pin
- ☐ Rooster
- ☐ Sailboat
- ☐ Shoe for rent
- ☐ Slippers (2)
- ☐ Spiderweb
- ☐ Stars (2)
- ☐ Telescope
- ☐ Tepee
- ☐ Turtle
- ☐ Yo-yo

# Search for Sam
## in
# Ancient Egypt
### and...

- ☐ Antenna
- ☐ Arrows (4)
- ☐ Blue hippo
- ☐ Boats (2)
- ☐ Boxes (3)
- ☐ Bucket
- ☐ Cats in bikinis (2)
- ☐ Chariot
- ☐ Falling coconuts (2)
- ☐ Fan
- ☐ Fire
- ☐ Fishing poles (2)
- ☐ Flying carpet
- ☐ Guard cats (5)
- ☐ Horse
- ☐ Jester
- ☐ Palm trees (2)
- ☐ Pyramids (8)
- ☐ Red birds (4)
- ☐ Red bow
- ☐ Rolled paper
- ☐ Sand pail
- ☐ Shovel
- ☐ Smiley face
- ☐ Snakes (2)
- ☐ Snowman
- ☐ Telephone
- ☐ Umbrella

# Search for Sam at the Cat Show and...

- ☐ Ball of yarn
- ☐ Bib
- ☐ Bones (2)
- ☐ Broom
- ☐ Camera
- ☐ Coconuts (2)
- ☐ Cow
- ☐ Cracked wall
- ☐ Cymbals (2)
- ☐ Fish bones (4)
- ☐ Graduate
- ☐ Guitar
- ☐ Hearts (3)
- ☐ Joggers (2)
- ☐ Lion
- ☐ Man in a cat suit
- ☐ Net
- ☐ Newspaper
- ☐ Palm tree
- ☐ Pizza boxes (2)
- ☐ Red bow
- ☐ Red curtain
- ☐ Royal cat
- ☐ Ticket booth
- ☐ Tombstone
- ☐ Witch

## Search for Sam with the
# Dogbusters
## and...

- ☐ Balloon
- ☐ Birdhouse
- ☐ Bones (13)
- ☐ Bridge
- ☐ Broom
- ☐ Clown
- ☐ Crane
- ☐ Crocodile
- ☐ Detective
- ☐ Dogs in tree (2)
- ☐ Fish (4)
- ☐ Flag
- ☐ Flower
- ☐ Hollow log
- ☐ Horse
- ☐ Jack-o'-lantern
- ☐ Ladders (3)
- ☐ Lamppost
- ☐ Manhole cover
- ☐ Old tire
- ☐ Pizza box
- ☐ Saddle
- ☐ Sailboat
- ☐ Siren
- ☐ Surfboard
- ☐ Taxi
- ☐ Tent
- ☐ Tightrope walker
- ☐ Turtle
- ☐ Umbrella
- ☐ Wanted poster
- ☐ Witch

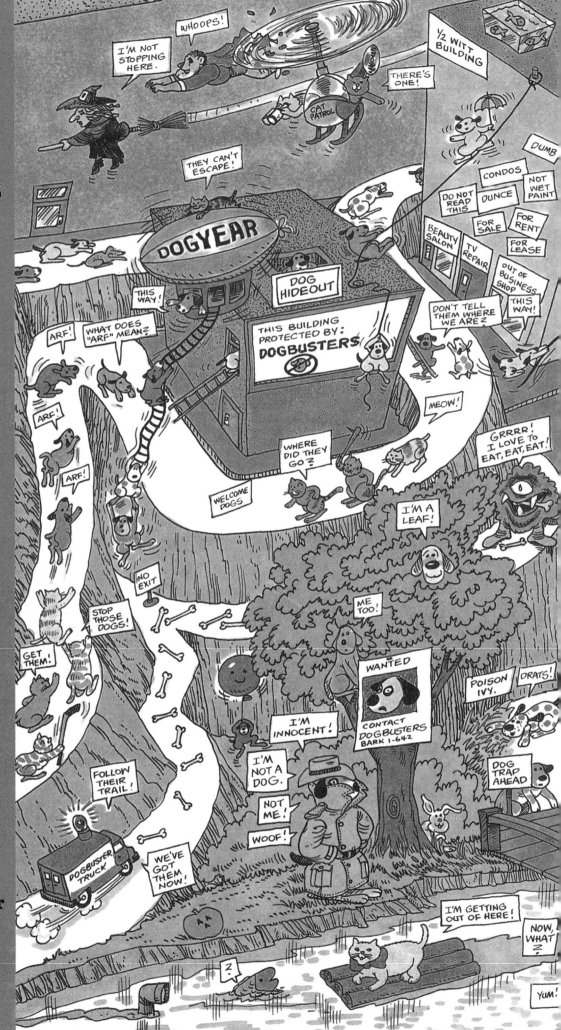

# Search for **Sam** at the **North Pole** and...

- ☐ Badge
- ☐ Bells (2)
- ☐ Bread
- ☐ Broken chair
- ☐ Cactus
- ☐ Campfire
- ☐ Chef's hat
- ☐ Clock
- ☐ Fish
- ☐ Fishing pole
- ☐ Football
- ☐ Globe
- ☐ Green sock
- ☐ Hammer
- ☐ Kite
- ☐ Locomotive
- ☐ Miner's hat
- ☐ Music notes (3)
- ☐ Ornament
- ☐ Pizza
- ☐ Polar bear
- ☐ Reindeer
- ☐ Satellite dish
- ☐ Singing birds (2)
- ☐ Snake with a hat
- ☐ Stepladder
- ☐ Toy car
- ☐ Yo-yo
- ☐ Zebras (2)